Illustrated by Aldo Ripamonti

This edition published in 1999 by Kibworth Books
Imperial Road, Kibworth Beauchamp, Leics LE8 0HR, England

© 1999 Kibworth Books, English Edition
© 1997 Istituto Geografico de Agostini, Novara

ISBN 0-7239-0197-X
Printed in Singapore

The Stories of
JESUS

Original Italian text by
Elio Guerriero

Translated and edited by
Maureen Spurgeon

Special Editor and Religious Adviser:
Janet Gilbert

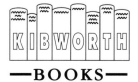
KIBWORTH
BOOKS

Introduction

It was hundreds of years ago that artists in eastern countries first began to create mosaic pictures of Christ, an art which is still practised today.

First, the surface of the picture is prepared, then the plan of the design is drawn. And as each part is filled in with tiny tiles of different colours, the figure of Jesus begins to appear.

In a similar way, God's plan of salvation was carefully prepared. This began with the coming of Jesus, and his birth in a stable at Bethlehem. Each year at Christmas, we remember the wonderful things which happened then, and the message of the angels, "Peace on Earth. Goodwill to all men."

Through his words, and his life on earth, Jesus still shows to us God's goodness and love and how this great love can free people from their sufferings.

The people of Israel had waited a long time for the coming of the Lord. The prophets Anna and Simeon who saw Jesus as a baby at the temple in Nazareth, knew that he was the Son of God, the Saviour who had come to earth to free people from the pain of sin and to grant forgiveness and mercy.

Later, the first disciples would see Jesus healing the sick, raising people from the dead and giving sight to the blind.

But all this made those in power distrust the Lord. And when they saw how ordinary people listened to what Jesus said and watched what he did, the scribes, the pharisees and the Roman governors turned against him. Jesus was not afraid to tell them when they were being unjust or cruel, or to show how much he loved the people who were under their control and wanted to help them.

It was this love for the people which led Jesus to the cross. And in the grave provided by Joseph of Arimathea, it seemed that the hopes of good people, the words of Abraham, Moses, the prophet Simeon and all those who believed in the coming of the Messiah, God's chosen one, were buried along with the body of the Lord.

Then on Easter Day, Jesus appeared again to his disciples. By proving that he had conquered death and risen again, he shows that each of us can live again after death, if we believe in Jesus, and let him come into our hearts as our Saviour.

The Hope of Israel

The birth of a baby comes at the end of a long time of waiting, something which many people have been hoping for. God is part of that long wait. He gave life to Mankind and a baby is proof that his gift of life continues and his love is given to us all. It was because God loved us that he sent his son to save us from our sins. When Jesus was born, it was God who prepared the way, God who gave the great news to the shepherds close at hand and sent the star to guide the three kings far away. Now, those on earth would be able to hear the word of the Lord, to know of his great love and learn to love him in return.

God Prepares for the Coming of Jesus

About one thousand years before the birth of Jesus, there lived in Israel a man called Elkanah and his two wives, Perinnah and Hannah. Perinnah had two children, but Hannah, the wife Elkanah loved most, had none.

Each year, the family went to the temple to offer a sacrifice to God. One year, Perinnah taunted Hannah so much about not having any children that she could not eat or sleep. Elkanah told her not to worry about it, but Hannah felt unhappy.

She went into the temple. "Dear God," she prayed, "do not forget me. Give me a child and I will dedicate his life to serve you."

An old priest whose name was Eli had seen Hannah praying. "Go home," he told her. "God will answer your prayer."

At once, Hannah began to smile. She believed what Eli said and her faith in God was rewarded. Within a year, she had given birth to a son, and called him Samuel.

When he was old enough, she took him to the temple. "Do you remember me?" she said to Eli. "I prayed for a child and you said God would answer my prayer. This is my son, Samuel. I promised to do all I could to dedicate his life to serving the Lord."

After that, Samuel stayed at the temple. And each year, Hannah would bring her son a fine new robe she had made for him.

Years passed and when Eli died, it was Samuel's task to lead the people of Israel, teaching them to pray and to worship the one true God.

Then one day, when Samuel himself was an old man, God told him to go to Bethlehem and see a man called Jesse. One of his sons, God said, would be the future king of Israel.

Seven of Jesse's sons came to meet Samuel, but God chose none of them. "There is only my youngest son, David," Jesse told Samuel. "He is looking after the sheep." Samuel told Jesse to send for him, and the moment Samuel saw him, God said, "Yes. This is the one."

The shepherd boy from Bethlehem became a great king. And through the family of David, a young man called Joseph would be born hundreds of years later and bring his young wife, Mary, to Bethlehem.

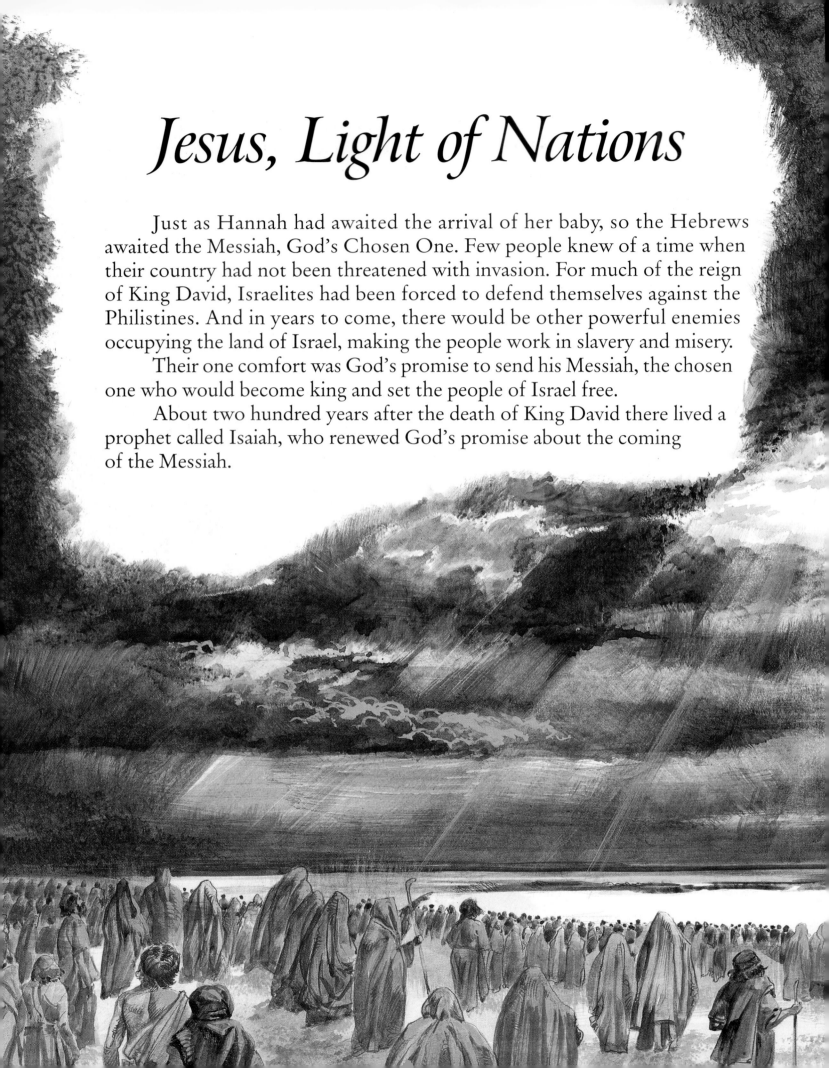

Jesus, Light of Nations

Just as Hannah had awaited the arrival of her baby, so the Hebrews awaited the Messiah, God's Chosen One. Few people knew of a time when their country had not been threatened with invasion. For much of the reign of King David, Israelites had been forced to defend themselves against the Philistines. And in years to come, there would be other powerful enemies occupying the land of Israel, making the people work in slavery and misery.

Their one comfort was God's promise to send his Messiah, the chosen one who would become king and set the people of Israel free.

About two hundred years after the death of King David there lived a prophet called Isaiah, who renewed God's promise about the coming of the Messiah.

Isaiah was also a wonderful poet who could use words to create mental pictures to show people all that God had promised. When the Messiah came, Isaiah said, his coming would be like a light for the people who walked in darkness: like a wonderful harvest, where everyone who was hungry would have enough to eat. When the Messiah came, it would be a time of great joy and happiness.

"The people who walked in darkness have seen a great light:
those who lived in a land of deep darkness, on them light has shined.
You have multiplied the nation, you have increased its joy;
They rejoice before you as with joy at the harvest.
For a child has been born for us, a son given to us."

Isaiah 9: 1-2, 5

The Annunciation

Hundreds of years after Isaiah, there lived in Nazareth a young woman called Mary. Nazareth is still only a small town in Galilee, to the north of Jerusalem. Mary and Joseph, the man she had promised to marry, were both descendants of the great King David. But at that time, the Roman Empire was the ruling power, and all the people of Israel were poor.

One day, Mary was alone in her little home, when she heard the voice of the angel Gabriel, who had been sent by God.

"Mary," the angel said, "of all the women in the world, you are the most favoured."

Seeing the angel in his white robes, Mary did not know what to do. What could this strange visit mean?

"Don't be afraid, Mary," Gabriel told her. "God is very pleased with you. That is why he has chosen you to be the mother of his son. You will name him Jesus. He will be great and will be called the Son of the Most High, and God will give him the throne of his ancestor, King David."

Gabriel was silent, waiting for an answer. Mary thought of God's promise to Israel, the child who the prophet Isaiah had said would be born and set the people free. Could it really happen, that she was going to be his mother?

"How is it possible?" she asked Gabriel. "I am not yet married. I have never lain with a man."

"The Holy Spirit will come down on you," explained Gabriel. "Your child will be called the Son of God."

Mary understood.

"Then, all is well," she said. "I am the servant of the Lord. I will do what he has asked of me."

The Visit to Elisabeth

When the angel Gabriel had gone, Mary must have spent a lot of time thinking about all that he had said would happen.

Gabriel had also told Mary that her cousin Elisabeth was already expecting a baby, even though she and her husband were both old and it had seemed impossible that they would ever have any children.

Mary decided to go and visit Elisabeth, to see the work of God in giving her a child and to share her wonderful news.

Elisabeth's home was some distance from Nazareth, and Mary's journey on foot took many days. For safety's sake, she would probably have followed behind a caravan, a line of donkeys or camels often loaded with spices from the countries east of Israel.

It was the job of Israelite slaves to walk alongside the animals, protecting the precious cargo from thieves. These slaves were often treated harshly by their masters, the merchants who rode on horseback.

To avoid the midday heat, long journeys were usually made during the early morning and then late afternoon, so that travellers could benefit from the cool morning dew on their skin, and also the breezes which blew across Galilee before the sun set.

The two women were so glad to meet each other at the end of Mary's tiring journey.

"How wonderful to see you, Mary!" cried Elisabeth. "You, the woman who is to be the mother of my Lord, coming to visit me!"

Mary was so happy, she burst into a song of joy and thankfulness. She had never doubted what Gabriel had said. Now, Elisabeth's words had made her doubly sure of the truth of all he had told her.

Mary's song begins "My Soul Doth Magnify The Lord". It can be read in the Gospel according to St. Luke, Chapter 1, verses 46-55.

The Birth of Jesus

JOSEPH TAKES MARY TO BETHLEHEM

Mary stayed with Elisabeth for three months before returning home to Nazareth. But when she told Joseph that she was going to have a baby, he was confused and upset, wondering what he should do.

But God watches over all his servants. He sent an angel to the young man in a dream, bringing him a special message.

"Joseph, son of David, do not be afraid to take Mary as your wife. The child which she is expecting was conceived through the Holy Spirit. She will bear a son, and his name will be Jesus. He will save his people from their sins."

Then Joseph understood. It was all as the prophet Isaiah had said.

"A virgin will conceive and bear a son, and they shall name him Emmanuel, which means 'God is with us'."

And so, Joseph took Mary as his wife, glad to be given the precious task of taking care of her and protecting the baby who was to be born.

SHE WRAPS HIM IN SWADDLING CLOTHES AND LAYS HIM IN A MANGER

For many years, Israel and the whole of Palestine had been under the control of Rome, and the Emperor Augustus had ordered a

18

census so that he could count up all the people who had to pay tax. The Emperor said that the head of each family must return to the place where they had originally come from, and put their names on a register.

Joseph was a descendant of King David, whose family had come from Bethlehem, a place some distance from Jerusalem. So, Joseph had to go there with Mary, who had only just a few days before she was due to give birth to her baby. But so many people had come to Bethlehem for the census that everywhere was crowded. People were coming and going, and all around were the soldiers of King Herod, the man chosen by the Romans to enforce their law.

When the time came for Mary to give birth, there was no room for the young couple at any inn. The only shelter was a stable, a cave in the hillside where animals were kept. And it was here that Mary gave birth to Jesus. Then, she wrapped him in strips of cloth – "swaddling bands" – and laid him in a manger.

THE SHEPHERDS WORSHIP JESUS

Nearby, shepherds were watching over their sheep in the cold night air. Suddenly they saw a great light. They were all very frightened, but the voice of an angel calmed them.

"Do not be afraid. I come to bring you news of great joy. Today is born in the City of David, a Saviour who is Christ the Lord. You will find him wrapped in swaddling bands and lying in a manger."

Then the sky seemed to open up, and the heavens filled with angels. "Glory to God in the highest," they sang out, "and on earth peace and goodwill to men."

"The City of David!" said the shepherds. "That's Bethlehem! We must go there and see what has happened, this great news which the Lord has told us about." And so they went to the stable and, as the angel had said, they found Mary and Joseph, with baby Jesus, lying in a manger.

The shepherds also told Mary and Joseph all that the angels said, that the Saviour had been born. And after they had stayed a little while, the shepherds went away again, praising God and thanking him for sending his Messiah.

THE OX AND THE ASS

Animals would almost certainly have been in the stable when Jesus was born. It was their resting place at night-time, as well as a place where they could be safe from thieves. And it was their feeding-box, the manger, in which Jesus was laid.

The ox and the ass were both valuable to ordinary people, and shelter for them would have been more important than for any other animals. Oxen were used for farming, and asses carried heavy loads as well as carrying those who could not afford horses.

This is why there is a general belief that there was an ox and an ass present at the birth of Jesus, the animals welcoming and helping to protect him.

Jesus, the Salvation of Israel

Mary and Joseph obeyed the words of the angel Gabriel, which had been given by God. When the baby was eight days old, he was given the name Jesus, which means 'God saves'.

Then came the time for Mary and Joseph to present Jesus at the temple in Jerusalem. The custom in those days was to offer a sacrifice, in thanksgiving, which was two doves.

In Jerusalem there was a very holy man named Simeon. He had spent many years in the temple, waiting for the coming of the Messiah. Now, he was old, but God had told Simeon that he would not die until he had seen the Messiah.

When he went into the temple and saw Joseph and Mary with Jesus, Simeon was filled with the Holy Spirit. He took the baby in his arms.

"Now," he said, "I can die in peace, Lord, because I have seen the Saviour."

There was another person in the temple, a prophetess named Anna, who stayed there praying day and night.

Like Simeon, she was very old, and filled with the Holy Spirit, so she knew that Jesus was God's chosen one, the Saviour who had been promised for so long.

After she had seen Jesus, she praised God, telling everyone she met of the wonderful news, that the Saviour had been born.

23

The Wise Men

The shepherds were not the only people to know of the birth of Jesus.

Far away to the east, three wise men were watching the night skies when they saw the most beautiful star. In ancient times, it was believed that such a star proclaimed the birth of someone very important. So the wise men decided to follow the star to see who had been born.

They followed it for a long, long time, but when they came to Jerusalem, the star could no longer be seen. "Where is the child who has been born King of the Jews?" they asked. "We have seen his star in the east and have come to worship him!"

Their words worried Herod, the king put in charge by the Romans. He called the chief priests and the scribes, asking them where the prophets had said the Messiah was to be born. "In Bethlehem," they said. So Herod sent the three wise men there. "And when you have found the child," said Herod, "come and tell me where he is so that I may go and worship him, too."

24

Just as the three wise men were leaving Jerusalem, so the star appeared again. They followed it until it came to the stable where Jesus lay. It was the end of their long journey.

The three wise men went inside and fell on their knees, offering the baby gifts of gold, frankincense and myrrh.

But before they left Bethlehem, God sent word to each of the wise men in a dream, saying that they should not go and tell Herod where Jesus was.

At the same time, God appeared to Joseph in a dream with an important message. "You must take the child and his mother into Egypt, and stay there until I tell you. Herod wants to find the child and put him to death."

It was only after Herod had died that an angel told Joseph and Mary it was safe to return to Israel and their little home in Nazareth.

Jesus at the Temple

Joseph settled in Nazareth, earning his living as a carpenter. He would have made objects like screens, doors and beams for the houses of rich people, but such work was not well paid, and the family would have been poor.

In those days, Hebrews liked to go to the temple at Jerusalem to celebrate Passover. This was the special meal shared by the Hebrews at the time of Moses, before God released them from slavery in Egypt.

When Jesus was twelve years old, he went on the long walk to Jerusalem with Mary and Joseph for the Feast of Passover, to pray to God at the temple and to share in the sacrifice of a lamb. At the time of the first Passover, the angel of the Lord "passed over" all homes where he saw the blood of a lamb which had been sacrificed, because these would have been the homes of Hebrew families who were to be released from slavery. But in the homes of the Egyptians, their captors, the eldest child died.

The Feast of the Passover lasted eight days. Then Joseph and Mary joined the other people returning to Nazareth. But they had lost Jesus!

At first, they searched for him among the people. Then, anxious and worried, they went back to Jersualem to look for him.

After searching for three days, Mary and Joseph found Jesus in the temple.

There, the boy sat among the priests, asking questions and answering with such wisdom that they were all amazed.

"My son!" Mary cried out. "Why have you done this? Your father and I have been so worried, searching everywhere for you."

Jesus always showed respect to Mary.

"Why do you search for me?" he said gently. "Do you not know that I must be about my Father's business?"

And so, although Jesus had been sent to live among ordinary people, he knew, even as a boy, that he was the Son of God.

The Ministry of Jesus

St. Luke tells us of the time when Jesus went to Jerusalem to celebrate Passover as a 12 year old boy. After that, there is little more recorded about his life until about eighteen years later. But it was usual for sons to follow the same trade as their fathers, so it is likely that Jesus learned the skills of carpentry from Joseph. St. Luke also says that Jesus "increased in wisdom" and we know that he learned to read and write. He would also have spent time in prayer and the study of the holy scriptures of the Old Testament. At the age of about thirty, he would begin his ministry among the people, travelling around to spread the good news about the coming of the Kingdom of God.

The Baptism of Jesus

Some months before Jesus was born, Elisabeth, Mary's cousin, had given birth to a son. She named him John. As a man he became known as John the Baptist, because he baptised people in the River Jordan.

John the Baptist was God's messenger, the person who told people that they must repent of their sins and prepare for the coming of the Saviour. "The Kingdom of God is at hand," John declared to the crowds who came to listen to him. "Prepare the way of the Lord!" Could John the Baptist be the long-awaited Messiah? Some people believed he was.

"No, I am not the Messiah," he told them. "The one who comes after me, I am not worthy even to undo his shoe laces."

One day, Jesus came to hear John the Baptist preaching and to be baptised. Of course, John knew that Jesus was the Son of God who had come to save free people from their sins.

"You come to me, asking to be baptised?" he said to Jesus. "I should be the one asking you to baptise me!"

But Jesus told John that he wanted to be baptised, just like anyone else. And so, they entered the waters of the River Jordan together.

Afterwards, Jesus returned to the banks of the river and began to pray. Suddenly, the heavens opened, and a dove which represented the Holy Spirit came down and rested on Jesus. Then a voice said, "This is my Beloved Son, in whom I am well pleased."

The baptism of Jesus shows that God is one in three persons – God the Father, God the Son and God the Holy Spirit and that Jesus is the Son of God.

Jesus Overcomes the Temptations of the Devil

Before beginning his ministry, or preaching, John the Baptist had spent many years in the wilderness, or desert, somewhere he could be alone to pray to God and to prepare himself for the task which lay ahead.

After his baptism, Jesus was also led by the Holy Spirit into the desert, to rest and to be alone with God.

For forty days and nights Jesus fasted, going without food or drink. At the end of that time, he was hungry, and knowing this, the devil came and tried to tempt him to use his power to obtain food.

"If you are the Son of God," said the devil, "command that these stones become bread."

Jesus answered by quoting words from the Bible. "Man does not live by bread alone, but by every word that comes from the mouth of God."

Then the devil led Jesus up a high mountain and showed him all the kingdoms of the world.

"All this I will give you," the devil said, "if you will fall down and worship me."

Jesus answered, "Worship the Lord your God and serve only him."

The devil tried a third time. He took Jesus to the top of a high temple.

"If you are the Son of God, prove it. Throw yourself down, so that the angels of God will save you, as the Scripture promises," the devil said cunningly.

But Jesus refused to fall into his trap. Instead, he quoted another truth from the Bible to defeat Satan. He said, "Do not put the Lord your God to the test."

(Luke 4: 1-12)

The Temptation of Jesus shows us that he knew only too well how it feels to be so weak that it seems we do not have the strength and the will to do the things that we should. There is nothing which any of us suffers that he did not suffer, too. Knowing that he understands our failings, we can put our faith and trust in him to help us overcome our own temptations.

Jesus Calls his Disciples

Soon after Jesus came out of the wilderness, he heard that the Judean king, Herod Antipas, had put John the Baptist in prison. Soon, his cousin would be killed and his work would come to an end. It was time for Jesus to spread the word of God and tell people how their sins could be forgiven.

There were plenty of people to listen to him around the Sea of Galilee. At 21 kilometres long, 12 kilometres wide and well below sea level, the lake had plenty of fish, with palms, olives and citrus fruits growing all around. People treasured it for their food and their livelihood.

It was at Capernaum, to the northwest of Galilee, that Jesus began his ministry, proclaiming God's love. Soon, people with disabilities and illnesses were brought to him and as Jesus laid his hands on each one, so they were cured. People came to know about Jesus, and crowds began to follow him.

On the shores of the lake one day, Jesus saw some fishermen washing their nets. He went up to one of them, Simon, and asked if he could come into his boat. Simon helped Jesus on board, then took him to the centre of the lake so that everyone could hear him. When he had finished preaching, Jesus said, "Go out into the deep water!" Simon obeyed. Then Jesus said, "Now, let down your nets!" Simon hesitated. He and his brother, Andrew, had spent the night fishing but had caught nothing.

"Master," said Simon, "we have worked all night and caught nothing. But we will do as you say."

The nets were lowered. And soon, such an enormous quantity of fish had been caught, that James and John, their friends in another boat, had to come and help them, both boats weighed down by the catch of fish. Simon fell down at the feet of Jesus.

"Leave me, Lord," he cried. "I am a sinful man."

"Do not be afraid," Jesus told him. "From now on, you will be a fisher of men."

And so Simon, Andrew, James and John became the first disciples of Jesus.

The Wedding at Cana

A little while after Jesus began his preaching, he was invited to a wedding at Cana, a small town halfway between Capernaum and Nazareth. Also sharing in the celebrations were Mary, his mother, some of his disciples... so many people, that the wedding party soon ran out of wine.

"They have no wine!" Mary told Jesus.

"What can I do?" he asked.

Mary turned to the servants. "Just do whatever he asks you to do," she told them.

At the entrance to the room there stood six big stone jars which had been filled with water so that people could wash their hands before the meal. Now, the vases were empty.

Jesus said to the servants, "Fill these with water!" And when they had done this he said, "Now, take them to the Master of the Table!"

The servants did all that Jesus said. And when the water was poured out, it had become wine.

The Master of the Table turned to the bridegroom. "You should have served the best wine first," he told him. "Then, when people had drunk that, served the wine which was not so good. You saved the best wine until last."

Only Jesus and the servants who had filled the stone jars with water knew what had happened. They realised that they had seen a miracle.

This lovely story recounts the first recorded miracle of Jesus, a gesture of kindness and courtesy, as well as a sign of the goodness of God.

Jesus Cures a Paralysed Man

As well as preaching in the open air, Jesus often liked to go into the homes of his followers. It was a way of having smaller gatherings, so that people could get close to him, as well as avoiding the heat when the sun was strongest. One day, he went into a house at Capernaum. But so many people had heard where he was that they all crowded inside wanting to see him and to hear all that he said.

A man who was completely paralysed and unable to move wanted to see Jesus so much that four of his friends carried him to the house on a stretcher. But there were so many people that they could not get inside the door.

But the man was determined. So his friends went around to the back of the house and found a way of getting up to the roof. In those days, houses were built quite low, so they were able to hoist the man up on his stretcher.

Next, they removed the tiles from the roof of the house, and, slowly and carefully, they lowered the sick man until he was right in front of Jesus. Seeing such faith, Jesus was moved. He stopped his preaching and turned to the man on the stretcher.

Jesus said, "Man, your sins are forgiven."

Some of the learned men and the scribes who were there wanted to protest. "What is this man saying?" they thought to themselves. "Only God can forgive sins!"

Jesus knew exactly what they were thinking. "What is wrong?" he asked them. "Is it easier to say, 'Your sins are forgiven,' or to say, 'Get up and walk'?" The scribes did not answer. Jesus went on, "So that you will know that the Son of God can forgive sins, I say to this paralysed man – 'Stand, roll up your stretcher and walk!' "

Hardly knowing what he was doing, the man obeyed. He got to his feet, rolled up the stretcher and began walking. We can imagine the wonder of everyone there. At first they had not understood what was happening. Now, they gave thanks to God, and said, "Today we have seen a miracle."

By performing this miracle, Jesus answered the scribes. They said, correctly, that only God could forgive sins. But no person could make a paralysed man walk, either. So, by using his power as the Son of God to heal the man, Jesus showed he could also forgive sins.

The Sermon on the Mount

Towards the north of Capernaum, the country rises up into hills to form a natural open-air theatre. It was here that Jesus came with his twelve disciples, including Simon and Andrew, James and John, followed by people who wanted to hear him. Then he sat and said some of his best-known words, which came to be called the "Sermon on the Mount". This was his plan, setting out the new things he was preaching about. These lines are called "Beatitudes", meaning blessings – each one begins with the word "Blessed".

Blessed are the poor in spirit, for theirs is the Kingdom of Heaven.
Blessed are those who mourn, for they shall be comforted.
Blessed are the meek, for they shall inherit the earth.
Blessed are those who hunger and thirst for righteousness,
for they will be filled.
Blessed are the merciful, for they will receive mercy.
Blessed are the pure in heart, for they will see God.
Blessed are the peacemakers, for they will be called the children of God.
Blessed are those who are persecuted for righteousness' sake,
for theirs is the Kingdom of Heaven.

Matthew 5: 3-10

To people then, as now, it seemed that the rich, the strong and the powerful were the ones who were blessed. But these eight beatitudes tell us how to be truly blessed and to live like Jesus.

Then, Jesus said, "Love your enemies, do good to those who hate you, bless those who curse you." He is saying that those who are truly blessed are those who follow his example, who become his disciples and follow him. A disciple of Jesus does not mind about forgiving insults. They are happy because they do not waste time in feeling bitter, jealous or unforgiving, or in allowing these feelings to make them discontented and spoil their lives.

It is this love which makes us true disciples of Jesus. He likened this love to the light of a candle.

"Nobody lights a candle then hides it," he said. "Instead, it is put in a candlestick to give light to the whole house. Let your light shine in the same way, so that others can see your good works and glorify God."

Jesus Cures the Centurion's Servant

At the time of Jesus, it was usual to see Roman soldiers in Palestine. With their well-trained armies they kept the people under the control of the Roman Empire, a very important task in a country where fights and rebellion against the Romans often arose. Sometimes the soldiers would work in small groups for local rich people, who paid them for keeping order.

This was the case of a certain centurion, a Roman officer who was well-known in Capernaum for his goodness and generosity. He had settled in Israel and very much admired the religion of the Hebrews, so different to that of the pagans in Rome. He had even helped the local people to build a synagogue.

This centurion had never met Jesus, but he had heard about the man who could work miracles and cure sick people. So when his faithful servant became seriously ill and was about to die, he knew of only one person who could save him. He hurried out to meet Jesus as he came into Capernaum.

"My Lord," he said, "my servant is at home, dying."

"I will come and heal him," Jesus told the centurion.

But to his surprise, the man answered, "Lord I am not worthy for you to come under my roof. Just say the word and I know my servant will be healed."

Jesus was amazed at these words. He turned to everyone there and said, "I tell you, not even in Israel have I found such faith."

And when they reached the house, the servant had been cured.

This miracle is important because it shows that Jesus makes no distinction between Hebrews, Romans or any others. He wants to serve all people who trust and put their faith in him.

The Feeding of the Five Thousand

After teaching his disciples, Jesus gave them special gifts, such as the gift of healing. This was so that people would believe that they were speaking God's truth. He sent them into the neighbouring countries of Palestine. They went in pairs – Simon and Andrew, James and John, Philip and Bartholomew. Later, the disciples were also called "apostles", meaning "chosen of Christ".

Everywhere they went, the disciples preached the word of Christ. They told people about Jesus of Nazareth, who showed his love by his care, by healing sick people and the miracles he worked. They explained that Jesus was not a king with powerful armies, as their ancestors had expected. Instead, he was gentle and kind, wanting only to save people from their sins with his great love. But not everyone listened to them.

Some people thought their words too simple to be true, others were too busy to listen, some were just not interested. But for those who listened there began a new hope and a new faith.

By the time the disciples returned to the Master, they were tired after their journeying and the work that Jesus had given them to do. Jesus noticed their weariness.

"Let us go somewhere quiet," he said, "so that you can rest yourselves a little." Simon and Andrew, James and John and the others welcomed this invitation, because they rarely had the chance to speak alone with Jesus. But before long, people saw Jesus and a crowd began to follow.

The disciples went into their boats moored in the harbour, and sailed out. But the people followed, hurrying around the banks to keep Jesus in sight.

Every so often a disciple would call to people in another boat or greet a passing boatman – whilst, on the water, the sun created a thousand reflections of people all around the lake.

Not far from the mouth of the river Jordan, Jesus and the disciples came ashore. But there were so many people waiting that Jesus felt sorry for them. He had wanted to be alone, but he also saw how much they wanted to hear his words.

Five thousand people listened. And as he preached, hardly anyone noticed the hours that were passing and the shadows lengthening on the lake.

At last the disciples said to Jesus, "Tell the crowd to return home. They have eaten nothing since morning."

But Jesus answered, "No. We must find food to feed them."

Then Andrew, Simon Peter's brother, spoke. "There is a lad here who has five barley loaves and two fishes. But how will that feed all these people?"

"Make them sit down in groups on the grass," Jesus decided.

The people obeyed. Then Jesus took the loaves and the fishes, lifted his eyes to heaven and blessed the food. He broke the loaves and handed the bread to the apostles for them to give to the people in the crowd. Not only was there enough food for everyone, but when the disciples collected up all that remained, there were enough left-overs to fill twelve baskets.

The Feeding of the Five Thousand is recounted in all four gospels of the New Testament – Matthew, Ch.14, 13-21; Mark, Ch.6, 34-45; Luke, Ch.9, 10-17 and John, Ch. 6, 5-13. The story is often told, not only because of the facts, but also because of what it signifies. Jesus is the Good Shepherd. He leads his flock to a special place, then takes care of them and breaks bread in the name of God. It is not only bodily care which he offers, but spiritual care, even life everlasting. As his ancestor David says in Psalm 23:

The Lord is My Shepherd:
I shall not want:
He makes me to lie down in green pastures;
He leads me beside the still waters; he restores my soul;
He leads me in right paths for his name's sake.
Even though I walk through the darkest valley, I fear no evil.
For you are with me; your rod and your staff, they comfort me.
You prepare a table before me in the presence of my enemies;
You anoint my head with oil;
my cup overflows.
Surely goodness and mercy shall follow me all the days of my life,
And I shall dwell in the house of the Lord for ever.

You are the Son of God

After preaching in the countries around Galilee, Jesus followed his disciples north, towards the city of Caesarea, where the shadow of Mount Hebron cooled the heat of the day.

These days of journeying, following the course of the River Jordan, gave Jesus time to explain more of his teaching to the disciples. As they came to the entrance of the city, almost as if to check what they had learned, Jesus asked them a question.

"Who do you say that I am?" They answered: "Some say you are John the Baptist, come to preach forgiveness through baptism. Others say you are the great prophet of ancient times, Elijah. Others say you are Jeremiah, or one of the other prophets."

Simon was the last to speak. He felt that he knew the answer. But he wanted to make it exactly right. How could he express the love of Jesus, the Saviour's wish to bless each sinner and bring joy to each man?

In the end Simon said, "You are Christ, Son of the Living God."

Jesus was surprised. Simon had expressed the great truth, known only to God the Father. He said, "You are truly blessed, Simon, son of Jonah, because my Father has revealed to you that I am his son. I say to you now that I shall call you Peter, meaning stone, the rock on which I will build my church."

This event is told in three of the gospels – Matthew Ch.16: 13-19; Mark Ch. 8: 27-30 and Luke Ch.9: 18-20. It tells us that the Christian faith is founded on the true belief that Jesus is the Son of God.

49

Love Thy Neighbour

Jesus was preaching in Jerusalem when a lawyer asked him, "What must I do to inherit eternal life? The scriptures say, 'You must love the Lord your God with all your heart and all your mind and all your soul and your neighbour as yourself.' But, who is my neighbour?"

Jesus answered by telling a special sort of story, called a parable. He told of a man going down from Jerusalem to Jericho (the lowest city in the world, 250 metres below sea level), when he was set upon by thieves. The man was wounded, his clothes ripped off and he was left for dead at the side of the road. By chance, a priest came along. Perhaps he felt sorry for the poor man, but he did not wish to get involved in the misfortunes of a stranger. And so he passed by on the other side. Then came a Levite, a member of the priesthood who served in the temple. He also wanted to avoid the bother of helping a sick man and so he, too, passed by on the other side.

Then a Samaritan came along. Samaritans were a race looked down on because they were not liked by the Jews. But he went up to the injured man, bound his wounds, then put him on his own donkey, took him to an inn and took care of him.

The following day when he had to continue his journey, he called the innkeeper and gave him money for their stay.

"Take care of him," the Samaritan said, "and whatever else you spend, I shall pay you back when I return."

After this story, Jesus asked the lawyer, "Which of those three, the priest, the Levite or the Samaritan, was the neighbour to the injured man?"

The lawyer was forced to admit, "The Samaritan."

Jesus said, "Then go and do the same."

This parable shows us that there are no limits to love. The person who is humble and the most despised can be the one nearest to God. So if we help that person instead of avoiding him or her, we help in the building of the Kingdom of God which reigns in peace and fellowship.

This is my Beloved Son

All through the journey back to Capernaum, Jesus seemed troubled. At last, he decided to tell his disciples what was on his mind. "I have to suffer and then die," he said. "On the third day, I shall rise again."

Some of the disciples were bitterly disappointed. They had followed Jesus ought about these words, we do not know. They had followed Jesus in the hope of taking part in the coming of his kingdom which they still thought included the overthrow of the Roman occupiers. Now, they did not know what to think, everything seemed to be destined to failure.

"Those who want to save their life shall lose it," Jesus continued, "but those who give their life for me shall find it. For what benefit will it be to them if they gain the whole world, but lose their life? What shall they give in return for their life?"

As they came to the lake at Capernaum, Jesus gave his disciples a few days rest, so that they could go and see their families. But Peter, James and John stayed with him. One afternoon, they went towards the mountain. Jesus walked away from them and began to pray. The three disciples were standing aside when suddenly they saw a strange sight. The face of Jesus began to shine, and his robes shone white. At one side of him appeared the figure of Moses, with Elijah at the other, showing the link between old and the new union between God and man.

"Master," Peter said, "if you wish, we will stay here and make three tabernacles, one for you, one for Moses and one for Elijah."

But even as Peter spoke, a bright cloud overshadowed them and there came a voice. "This is my beloved son, in whom I am well pleased. Listen to him." Peter had acknowledged Jesus as the Son of God. Now God had repeated that acknowledgment.

Seek Ye First
the Kingdom of God

Nothing escaped the watchful eyes of Jesus. As he went about, he noticed something which is still true today – how many people, fearing that one day they will be in want, become slaves to work and to money. They worry about storing up riches, but they do not have time to relax and to enjoy the good things which God gives us. They live their whole lives without ever finding time to thank God for his goodness or to look around at the wonderful earth which he created.

One day, a follower asked Jesus, "Will you talk to my brother and ask him to share his inheritance with me?"

"Beware of greed," Jesus replied. "A person's life does not consist of the things which that person owns."

And he told the story of such a man who had spent his whole life dreaming of becoming rich. He worked hard but he did not think of what God wanted him to do. The man bought a great deal of land and sowed the seed. As the seed grew and ripened into grain, the harvest was so good that it was necessary for him to build a bigger barn so that he could store it all.

And so the man fulfilled his dream of becoming rich. "At last," he said to himself, "you have all that you want. Now you can rest, you can eat, and be merry to your heart's content."

But that same night the man died. So he did not enjoy even for a single instant any of the things for which he had sacrificed his life.

This parable tells us that it is not the person who stores up treasure on earth who is rich in the sight of God. What is the use of worldly goods if a person is discontented and not at peace?
Jesus said, "Consider the lilies of the field. What could be more beautiful? If God takes care of them, will he not take care of you?"

God is Merciful to the Repentant Sinner

When Jesus lived on earth, his greatest enemies were the Jewish religious leaders, called pharisees and scribes. These men considered themselves perfect and pleasing to God. They hated Jesus because he called them sinners and undermined their authority. They often tried to trap him into errors by asking impossible questions.

One day, they brought to Jesus a married woman guilty of committing adultery, of loving another man. Spitefully they reminded him that the Law of Moses required that a woman guilty of adultery be stoned to death. "What do you say?" they asked Jesus. He did not answer. Instead, he began writing in the earth. "Well," they said again, "what do you say?"

Jesus replied, "He that is without sin among you, let him cast the first stone at her." Then he went on writing in the earth until, slowly and silently, they all began to move away. After all, who could say that they were without sin before him, who could see into their hearts and read their innermost thoughts?

When he and the woman were alone, Jesus rose to his feet and said, "Woman, where are the people who accused you? Has anyone condemned you?" And she answered, "No one, Lord." Then Jesus said to her, "Neither do I condemn you. Go and sin no more."

In this incident, related in John Ch.8, Jesus shows that God is concerned about what is in our hearts. The woman is an outcast to the Jews, but Jesus challenges the pharisees. He tells them – you can stone her, if you are not guilty of sin yourselves. When they cannot, he has compassion on the woman and says she can leave, but she must sin no more. God will not tolerate sin, but if we are sorry and trust in Jesus, then he is merciful.

The Good Shepherd

Centuries before Jesus, people had lived by farming or by rearing animals. The ancient Hebrews were shepherds and in their holy books they wrote of the dangers of caring for their flocks, often having to defend their animals with their lives. But as time passed, rich breeders employed hired hands, men who were paid to look after the sheep. Of course, a hired man did not take as much care as the owners. When danger threatened they would sooner run away than protect the animals.

The Old Testament prophets often used the example of a good shepherd, to describe the relationship between God and his people. They said that God is like the Good Shepherd, taking loving care of his people, chasing enemies away and then laying his people down to rest.

But the hired man is the false leader, and, like the hired shepherd, paid to look after the people. But in times of danger, this leader will leave them to their fate. In future times, the prophets said, there would come a Messiah who, like God the Father, would take care of his people, those who trust in Jesus as their Saviour, and not abandon them.

At the end of his public life, Jesus spoke of being that Good Shepherd whom the prophets had spoken of. He knows all his followers, and each one knows that they can speak to Jesus at any time. He would care for every single one and never leave them, even laying down his life. And because of this sacrifice, God will raise them from the dead and continue to take care of them in Heaven.

Jesus said:
"I am the Good Shepherd,
I know my sheep
and my sheep know me,
just as the Father knows me
And I know the Father;
and I lay down my life for the sheep.
Therefore, the Father loves me
because I lay down my life
that I may take it again."

John 10: 14-15 17

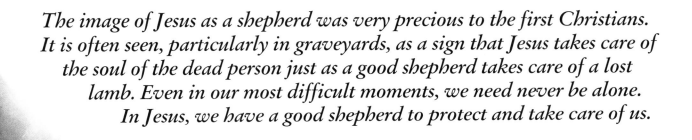

*The image of Jesus as a shepherd was very precious to the first Christians.
It is often seen, particularly in graveyards, as a sign that Jesus takes care of
the soul of the dead person just as a good shepherd takes care of a lost
lamb. Even in our most difficult moments, we need never be alone.
In Jesus, we have a good shepherd to protect and take care of us.*

No One Has Greater Love Than This

In his Gospel, St. John recounts how Jesus said to his disciples, "No one has greater love than this, to lay down one's life for one's friends. You are my friends." *(John 15:13/14)* This tells us that Jesus knew very well what was going to happen to him, but he was ready to face death. Through his work and his actions during his life on earth, Jesus showed that he looked upon all people as friends, just as much as his disciples, and he was ready to sacrifice his life for everyone. And by laying down his life, Jesus restores peace between God and those on earth.

The Resurrection of Lazarus

Jesus often stopped at Bethany, the home of a friend called Lazarus and his sisters, Mary and Martha. One day, the Master was preaching near Jerusalem, when there came a message to say that Lazarus was very ill.

Although Jesus loved Lazarus and his family and had the power to heal him, he stayed away. Three days later, he said to his disciples, "Our friend Lazarus is asleep. But I shall go and wake him." The disciples thought this meant that all was well. So Jesus told them plainly, "Lazarus is dead." The disciples were confused. How could Jesus wake him?

When they arrived, Mary and Martha were being comforted by friends. Lazarus had indeed been dead four days. Martha came out to meet Jesus.

"Lord," she said, "if you had been here, my brother would not have died!"

"I am the resurrection and the life," said Jesus. "Whoever believes in me shall live, even if he were dead. Do you believe me?"

"Yes," said Martha at last. "I believe that you are Christ, the Son of God." She went to her sister, and Mary's words were the same as Martha's. "Lord, if you had been here, my brother would not have died!"

Seeing her weeping, Jesus also began to cry. As they arrived at the grave, Jesus was very moved. Suddenly he ordered, "Take the stone away!" Martha tried to persuade him not to do this, but Jesus insisted.

Then Jesus cried out, "Lazarus, come forth." Moving stiffly, with his feet and his hands bandaged, according to the custom of the time, Lazarus came out of the tomb.

These things happened in this way so that Jesus could show, without any doubt, that he was the Son of God.

The Entry into Jerusalem

The time of the Passover was approaching. Hebrews from all over the Greek-Roman empire were arriving in the Holy City of Jersualem. They wanted to renew their unity with God and to keep watch throughout the holy night to celebrate the liberation of the Israelites from Egypt when God had freed his people from slavery.

A long line of people passed through Bethany, looking forward to seeing the wall and the temple of the City of David.

Jesus also wanted to celebrate Passover. About a week beforehand, at the Mount of Olives, he called two of his disciples. "Go into that village over there," he said, pointing, "and you will find a donkey. Untie the donkey and bring it to me. And if anyone asks you, just say that the Lord needs it."

The disciples did as Jesus asked. Then he mounted the donkey and took the road to Jerusalem. Many people saw this as a sign that the Messiah was coming and crowds soon formed along the road at the entrance to the city. Some believers threw down their cloaks on the ground, others cut down branches from the trees and spread them on the road, all crying out in chorus:

> "Hosanna to the Son of David!
> Blessed is he who comes in the name of the Lord.
> Hosanna in the highest!"

All this was enough to tell the men in power that Jesus was entering the city. They hated to see how crowds gathered to meet him and hear their cries of love and welcome. Some said Jesus should tell his followers not to greet him in such a way. "Why?" said Jesus. "What they say is true."

At the sight of the city, Jesus was sad. "If you had only recognised on this day the things that make for peace," he wept. "But now they are hidden from your eyes!"

Jesus went to the temple to pray. But inside there were merchants, men changing money for visitors from other lands, sellers of doves and cattle for sacrifice, all kinds of buying and selling. All this was not something to be done in the House of God, especially with the cheating and arguments which often took place.

Angrily, Jesus overturned the tables of the money-changers and the merchants. "My house shall be called the House of Prayer!" he cried. "But you have made it a den of thieves!"

Nobody spoke. None of the merchants or money-changers dared to challenge Jesus. This was too much for the men in authority. They saw Jesus as a threat, someone taking power away from them. So they began plotting to put him to death, in order to try and put an end to his influence on the people.

The Last Supper

A PLOT AGAINST JESUS

Jesus had told the disciples that he would be tried, put to death and rise again on the third day. They did not understand what he was saying. But the time was drawing near when everything would happen just as he had said.

The scribes and pharisees lost no time in meeting at the house of the high priest Caiaphas to discuss ways of taking him prisoner. They were very pleased when Judas Iscariot, one of the twelve disciples, came to see them, offering help.

"How much will you pay if I hand Jesus over to you?" he asked.

"Thirty pieces of silver," they offered. Judas agreed. He knew that Jesus often went to the Garden of Gethsemane at the end of the day. The plan was that he would kiss Jesus, so that the scribes could see which man to arrest.

But Jesus knew that he would be betrayed by one who for so long had sat at a table with him and shared a meal.

THE PREPARATIONS FOR THE PASSOVER

According to Jewish tradition, the Passover Supper was celebrated on the eve of the Saturday, in memory of the deliverance of the Hebrews from Egypt. But on the Thursday, while he was staying at Bethany, Jesus called Peter and John, his two best-loved disciples, and told them to proceed to Jerusalem and prepare the Passover Supper there, on that day.

Peter and John were probably surprised at this break in tradition. "Exactly where do you want us to prepare it?" they asked Jesus. The Lord's answer was very detailed. He said that they would meet a man with a jug in his hand. They were to follow him and go into a house and ask the man there to let them have a large room with everything that they needed. Obediently, Peter and John followed the orders, and found the supper room in Jerusalem, the place where Jesus would celebrate his last Passover.

Accompanied by all twelve disciples, he went to the house where Peter and John had hurriedly prepared the supper. He entered the room and sat down at the table with them.

The celebration which was about to begin followed an ancient and very precise pattern. The head of the family says a prayer and gives the "benediction" or blessing. Then comes the Supper in which the food is the same as that eaten by the first Hebrews when they left Egypt.

The Supper ends with a recitation of some psalms of thankfulness to God for the great work he did for his people.

It was within this old framework that Jesus introduced the ceremonies of the new faith and which formed the basis for people's new fellowship with God.

I HAVE LEFT YOU AN EXAMPLE

Knowing that he would soon die, Jesus wanted to leave his disciples signs to remember his life. St. John's Gospel *(13:1)* tells us "Having loved his own who were in the world, he loved them to the end."

When the disciples were all sitting down, Jesus got up from the table, took off his robe and tied a towel around himself.

Then, he took a basin, filled it with water and went to wash the feet of the disciples. They were almost speechless with surprise. "Lord, are you going to wash my feet?" protested Peter. "You will never wash my feet." But Jesus insisted, and after having washed the feet of all the disciples, explained: "Do you know what I have done? You call me Master and Lord and you speak right because that is what I am. So if I, your Lord and Master, have washed your feet, you also should wash one another's feet."

Jesus washing the disciples' feet was a sign of love as well as an example for them. He was showing that whatever he had done for them before his death, they must do for others during their own lives.

THE LAST SUPPER

After washing the feet of the disciples, the Passover Supper began.

"I wish to eat this Passover Supper with you before I suffer," said Jesus. "All that we are doing now, I want you to do when I am gone, so that you will remember me and how I died for you."

The disciples looked at each other. Could it really be true that Jesus was about to die? It did not seem possible.

Jesus took a piece of bread and gave thanks to God. Then he broke it and gave it to the disciples, saying, "This is my body, which is given for you. Do this in remembrance of me."

The Supper continued and Jesus poured wine into a cup. After a prayer of thanks, he said, "This cup which is poured out for you is my blood which is shed for you."

"Someone will betray me," Jesus went on. "He is sitting at this table."

"But, who is it?" Peter wanted to know.

"The one to whom I give this piece of bread dipped in the dish," Jesus answered. He gave the bread to Judas Iscariot. "Do what you are going to do," Jesus told him. "And do it quickly."

The disciples thought that as Jesus had earlier given Judas some money, the Lord was telling him to go out and buy all that they needed to celebrate the Festival of the Passover. Only Judas Iscariot knew the real truth.

"Lord," said Peter at last, "you know I would lay down my life for you."

"Would you, Peter?" Jesus answered. "Well, before the cock crows twice at the start of the new day, you will deny knowing me three times."

It seemed impossible that within just a few days Jesus would be put to death and that his most loyal disciple would deny ever knowing him.

"No," said Peter at last. "I would die with you. I would not deny you."

At Gethsemane

Leaving the room of the Last Supper, Jesus went with all the disciples, except Judas, to Gethsemane, a little way outside the city. The Hebrew name means "Press of Olives", so it was probably an olive grove with a press to extract the oil, perhaps protected by some sort of enclosure.

"Stay with me," Jesus told Peter, James and John. "Keep awake while I am here." He went away from them and began to pray. He knew of the cruel and painful death which awaited him. Which of his friends could he turn to? Who could fully understand all that he had to face? Only God could help him.

At last, he came back to his disciples and found them asleep. "Couldn't you stay awake for one hour with me?" he said to Peter.

Again, he prayed to God, so earnestly that the sweat on his forehead fell like drops of blood. "If this is your will, then your will must be done."

When he had finished, the disciples had fallen asleep. Jesus knew they were tired, so he went to pray. "Are you still sleeping?" he said to them when he returned. "Soon the hour will come when I shall be betrayed."

At that moment, Judas Iscariot came into the garden. He went up to Jesus to kiss him. "So, Judas," said Jesus, "is it with a kiss that you betray me?"

The three disciples saw then that Judas was leading a crowd of scribes and priests, lanterns held high so that they could see the man Judas kissed.

"Who are you looking for?" Jesus asked them.

"Jesus of Nazareth," they said.

"I am he," Jesus answered. As he spoke, the crowd all reeled back and fell to the ground as if they had been knocked down. "And if you are looking for me," he went on, "then let my disciples go." Now armed soldiers could also be seen, a clear sign that Jesus was to be taken prisoner.

Peter was angry. What had Jesus done to deserve this? In his rage, he reached for his sword and cut off the ear of the servant of a high priest.

"No more of this!" cried Jesus. "Peter put your sword away!" And despite all the uproar, he reached out and touched the ear of the servant to heal him.

Jesus had seen how cowardly the scribes and pharisees were, coming to take him prisoner at night. "You come for me with your swords and sticks as though I were a thief," Jesus said to them. "You would not have arrested me while I was preaching at the temple. But all this is what the ancient prophets said was going to happen."

Jesus is Condemned to Death

When Jesus was arrested, the disciples who were with him had run away in fright and confusion, not knowing what they were going to do. But Peter stayed, following at a distance as Jesus was led to the palace of the high priest Caiaphas. Here in the courtyard some servants were sitting beside a fire. Peter sat down too, and a maid saw him. "He was with Jesus of Nazareth," she said. Peter denied it, saying, "Woman, I do not know him."

Soon after, a similar question was asked by a man, a relative of the servant whose ear Peter had cut off. "Weren't you in Gethsemane with Jesus?"

"I've said I do not know him!" As Peter spoke, a cockerel crowed loudly.

"But you're from Galilee," a third servant persisted. "We can tell by your voice. You must be one of those who were with him!"

"No!" cried Peter again. "I don't know who you are talking about!"

The cockerel crowed a second time, and Peter remembered Jesus' words. "Before the cockerel crows twice, you will deny knowing me three times."

Peter felt so ashamed. He had told Jesus that he would never deny knowing him, yet this had happened. He went outside and wept bitterly.

By now the people who were to decide what was to happen to Jesus had arrived at the palace of Caiaphas. They told lots of lies about him, but Jesus said nothing. Then Caiaphas spoke.

"You say that you are the Messiah, the Son of God?"

"Yes, I am," Jesus answered.

"Do we need to hear any more?" exclaimed Caiaphas. "You have heard the blasphemy! He must be condemned to death!" But first Caiaphas had to obtain the consent of the Roman governor, Pontius Pilate. At first, Pilate sent Jesus to King Herod, who was in Jerusalem at the time, hoping that he would deal with him. Herod had heard of Jesus. Would he perform some miracle to free himself? But Jesus did nothing, nor did he answer any questions. So Herod told his soldiers to return him to Pontius Pilate.

Pilate knew Jesus was blameless. He brought a man called Barabbas from prison. "One prisoner may go free at Passover," Pilate told the accusers. "Will you choose Jesus, or Barabbas?" He thought they would choose Jesus.

"Barabbas!" they shouted. "Release Barabbas!"

"I can find no fault with Jesus," said Pilate. "What shall I do with him?"

"Crucify him!" they shouted. "Crucify him!"

Pilate dared not stand against them. Instead he washed his hands to show he would have nothing to do with what would happen. And so Jesus was condemned to die by a torture reserved for slaves and the lowest of people.

Jesus Dies on the Cross

After he had been condemned to death, Jesus was put into the charge of the Roman soldiers. To them crucifixions were an entertainment, a change from their duties. They had heard people calling the prisoner the King of the Jews, and some put a broken reed in his hand. Others threw a red robe around his shoulders, plaiting a crown of thorns and putting it on his head.

In his suffering, Jesus was scorned and alone. Soon he was stripped of his clothes and the arms of the cross on which he was to die tied to his shoulders.

Then a line of people, the Roman soldiers, Jesus, and two thieves who had been condemned to die at the same time as him, began making their way towards Calvary, a hill just outside the city wall of Jerusalem about 600 metres from the residence of the Roman Governor. It was a short journey, but a terrible trial to the condemned men on the way to the scene of their death.

Soon Jesus was exhausted, unable to go on. So the soldiers made a man called Simon, who came from Cyrene in North Africa, carry the cross for him. Among the crowds who followed were some women, weeping bitterly.

"Daughters of Jerusalem," said Jesus, "do not weep for me, but for yourselves and for your children."

When the procession reached Calvary, the prisoners were thrown to the ground and nailed to their crosses. Then they were tied to the wood and the crosses set upright.

People began to shout and jeer at Jesus, mocking him. Soldiers at the foot of the cross tore the Lord's robe and drew lots for the pieces.

Mary, his mother, was also there with his disciple, John, when the sun suddenly disappeared and it became so dark that many people were frightened.

It was dark for three long hours, and all that time Jesus hung on the cross, suffering great torture and pain. When he cried out with thirst, a soldier put a vinegar-soaked sponge at the end of a stick which he thrust at the mouth of Jesus.

Towards three o'clock in the afternoon, Jesus cried, "Father into your hands I commend my spirit." Then he died.

So Jesus had finished the work which God had sent him to do, as the Saviour who had come to forgive the sins of all those who put their faith and trust in him.

75

The New Life

After Jesus died, some of his friends stayed by the cross until it was dark. Then his body was taken down. A man called Joseph of Arimathea had gone to Pontius Pilate to ask for the body of Jesus. Although Joseph was a member of the Jewish council, he was also a follower of Jesus and wanted to provide a tomb for burial. In those days, tombs were usually caves or places cut from rock with a heavy stone in front. But the pharisees remembered Jesus saying that he would rise from the dead after three days and they made plans to watch the tomb, to make sure that nobody could remove the stone. But, the death of Jesus defeated death itself. God the Father resurrected him to a new life, and with his resurrection comes the promise of everlasting life for each believer. When a Christian dies, the family and friends are sad. But they have the certainty of that person living again in heaven and being together in a new life.

Jesus is Risen from the Dead

The arrest and crucifixion of Jesus had thrown his disciples into confusion and they had scattered around Jerusalem, not knowing what to do. But on the Sunday morning, after the Sabbath day of rest, three women went to the tomb provided by Joseph of Arimathea, to place spices and ointments among the burial linen in which the body of Jesus had been wrapped. One was Mary who came from Magdala, by the Sea of Galilee, and all three were worried about moving away the heavy stone which sealed the tomb. But they found that the stone had already been set aside, as if someone had been there before.

Mary Magdalene ran to tell Peter and John. "Someone has taken Jesus out of the tomb!" she told them. "And I don't know where they have laid him!"

The other women went inside. The body of Jesus was not there, but two angels stood beside the tomb. "Why do you search among the dead for he who is living?" they asked. "Jesus is not here. He is risen. Go and tell Peter and the other disciples!"

By the time Peter and John arrived, the women had gone. Seeing the burial linen by the tomb, they did not know what to think, quite forgetting Jesus had said he would rise from the dead. They went home. Mary Magdalene still thought that someone had taken the body of Jesus and she began to cry.

"Why are you crying?" came the voice of a man standing nearby. Mary Magdalene thought he was the gardener.

"Sir," Mary wept, "if you took him away, please tell me where you have laid him!"

"Mary." There was no mistaking the voice of Jesus. Mary was overjoyed.

"Master!" She reached out to touch him, as if she could not really believe that he was not dead, but living.

"Do not hold on to me," Jesus told her, "for soon I must go to heaven to be with my Father. Just tell my disciples what you have seen."

Stay With Us, Lord

A few hours after the discovery of the empty tomb, the news had spread among some of the disciples. But although they wanted to believe, many could not help doubting what they had heard and being sad at what had happened.

Towards evening, two disciples left for Emmaus, a village about 10 kilometres from Jerusalem.

As they walked, they were talking together of the suffering of Jesus of Nazareth, when a third person joined them and walked along following the rhythm of their steps. He listened for a while, then asked, "Who are you speaking about?" This question amazed the disciples. How was it that the stranger did not know? Nobody in Jerusalem had talked of anything else. One of them, a man called Cleopas, answered, "We speak of Jesus of Nazareth, a powerful prophet in all he said and did. We were all hoping that he was the Messiah sent by God, but the priests gave him over to the Romans to crucify him. Now some women in Jerusalem are saying that he has risen from the dead. Some other disciples have been to the tomb and found it empty, but we do not know what to think."

The stranger responded with a kindly reproach.

"Oh, how foolish you are! Why don't you believe what has happened? Didn't the scriptures say that he had to die and then return to life?"

The two disciples did not know how to answer. As they arrived at Emmaus, their fellow traveller was about to leave them, but the disciples wanted again to hear the words which had given them faith.

"Stay with us," they said, "because it is almost evening and the day is nearly over."

So, with the stranger following them, the disciples went indoors and soon prepared something to eat. When, at last, all three were sitting at the table, the guest pronounced a blessing, took bread, broke it and gave it to the two disciples. And at that moment, they knew it was Jesus.

They only saw him for a moment. When the two disciples looked again, the Master had gone . But that did not matter.

The two disciples believed what they had seen. The same evening they returned to Jerusalem, to tell Peter and most of the other disciples that Jesus had truly risen from the dead.

The Ascension of Jesus

Judas Iscariot was now dead, but the two men who had walked with Jesus along the road to Emmaus knew the house where Peter and most of the other disciples were. They were all inside, talking together, when Jesus suddenly appeared. He held out his hands towards them, showing the dreadful wounds where he had been nailed to the cross. They saw the marks of the nails on his feet and where his body had been pierced by the sword of a Roman soldier. Now, there could be no further doubt. Jesus had truly risen from the dead, just as he had said.

The disciples were so happy to see Jesus, to share a meal with him and to talk together. But Jesus knew that he would only remain on earth for a short time. Soon, as he had told Mary Magdalene, he would return to heaven to be with God, his Father.

The disciples saw Jesus twice after that. Then they all met together for the last time in the city of Jerusalem, and Jesus explained how his work was to continue. "I want you to go into the world and tell people about how I came to earth to forgive people their sins," he told them. "Do all that I have taught you, healing the sick, helping and giving comfort to people, baptising them in the name of the Father, the Son and the Holy Ghost. And no matter what happens, remember that I shall always be with you."

When he had finished speaking, Jesus led his disciples to Bethany. "When you go back to Jerusalem," he said, "the Holy Ghost will come down on you and give you the strength to do my work."

Then he reached out his hands to bless the disciples. And as they all looked at his face for one last time, Jesus was lifted up into a cloud and out of their sight.

The disciples went back to Jerusalem, as Jesus had told them. They were in a room when there came a sound like a great wind. People nearby ran inside, to find the disciples praying and worshipping God, tongues of fire above them, then speaking in different languages.

"Jesus told us he would send us the Holy Ghost," said Peter. "That is what you have seen today. Whoever believes in Jesus and is baptised in his name will receive the Holy Ghost, too."

So the life of Jesus had come to an end on earth. But he lives for evermore in heaven and all his disciples continue his work.

The Work Continues

In the Acts of the Apostles, *(Ch. 1, 9-11)* St. Luke tells us that after the Ascension of Jesus, his disciples stayed looking up at the sky. Suddenly, there appeared two angels. "Men of Galilee," they said, "why do you stay looking up towards heaven?"

The disciples knew what the angels meant. After his resurrection, Jesus had told them to go out to all nations, preaching his word and telling people of his life which he gave for them. So, instead of looking up at the sky, the time had come when they had to turn their attention towards earth, where people from many other countries had not heard of Jesus. And so those first disciples began journeying abroad, showing by their example the teaching of Jesus, praising God and helping people.

The Life of the First Christians

After the Ascension, the Christian faith began with the community of disciples of Jesus. In the Acts of the Apostles, *(Ch. 1.15)* St. Luke tells us that Peter spoke to about 120 disciples, but this number soon increased in Jerusalem and Galilee. Before long, there were Christians in Antioch, the capital of Syria, and disciples were journeying through the Middle East, then going across the Mediterranean Sea towards Europe.

One reason why Christianity spread so rapidly was that disciples followed the teaching of Jesus, sharing what they had and living in peace and fellowship, some of them working miracles to heal the sick just as Jesus had done. In the Acts of the Apostles, St. Luke reports on the three most important features in the lives of those first Christians as they gathered together in groups called churches.

THE HEARING OF THE WORD AND THE UNION OF FELLOWSHIP

The first Christians heard the good news of Jesus as their Saviour through the apostles. As they came to believe in Jesus Christ, the apostles then taught them what God wanted them to be like.

The results of that faith was soon seen by others. Christians showed their love for their fellow man by giving things to those who had more need of them. They also sold what they possessed, giving the money to the apostles so that they could distribute it among the poorest people.

THE BREAKING OF BREAD

At the Last Supper, Jesus had broken bread with the disciples and said, "Do this in remembrance of me."

In the Acts of the Apostles, *(Ch. 2.46)* St. Luke recounts how the first Christians broke bread together in each other's homes, as

a sign of fellowship and to remember the sacrifice of Jesus in giving his life for the sake of all those who believe in him .

PRAYER

Prayer is extremely important in Christian life, and it was especially so for the first Christians.

Jesus had given many examples of prayer during his life on earth. Often, the four gospels tell us, he went to the temple to pray, to give thanks to God and seek guidance.

But at other times, too, such as at the resurrection of Lazarus, on the Sea of Galilee and in the garden of Gethsemane, the Lord had shown that it was always possible to worship God and to seek his help.

With the example of Jesus to guide them, the early Christians knew the power and the comfort of prayer. It was an expression of praise and thanks to God for his great goodness in sending Jesus to earth, as well as a way of asking for strength in times of trial and weakness.

The Writings which are a Record of Jesus

In the Acts of the Apostles, St. Luke recounts the beginnings of the Christian community. After the arrest and death of Jesus, the disciples met together again and began to spread the name and the word of the Lord in Galilee and Jerusalem. This was very dangerous, especially in Jerusalem. As the years passed, disciples were often beaten, imprisoned, and then released on condition that they

would not even say the name of Jesus.

To this, St. Peter answered: "Whether it is right in God's sight to listen to you rather than to God, you must judge; for we cannot keep from speaking about what we have seen and heard." *(Acts 4: 19-20)*

Despite all this, the name of Jesus spread quickly and large Christian communities soon formed in Palestine and the surrounding lands. The ever-increasing numbers of Christians brought new challenges to the first disciples. They told people about the death of Jesus and his resurrection, but the new followers always wanted to know more about him. So the apostles told everyone the story of his life, his teaching, what the Old Testament prophets had written about his coming and all the wonderful things that they had seen. There was also the need to tell people in far countries about Jesus. The disciples could not be everywhere at once, so the Holy Spirit helped them to dictate to writers what they had seen and the things they had done. This means that the writings in the Bible are accurate and still relevant to Christians today.

Bible experts believe these writings about the life and preaching of Jesus began around the year 50 AD (20 years after his death). This was not long, considering the difficulties which faced those first writers, especially when they worked in places where there was distrust and persecution. At first, people dictated the actual words they had heard Jesus speak. Things which the disciples remembered followers saying to each other were also written down, as well as the accounts of all the most important parts of the life of Jesus, the account of his ministry, judgement, death and resurrection. Then came the need to use all these accounts to make a true picture of the life and teaching of Jesus. And so we have the beginnings of the Gospels, a word meaning "good news", the four books which begin the New Testament.

Then, because Christianity was spreading so quickly, the apostles and leaders of the community wrote letters to explain to new disciples the teaching of Christ, his instructions on the way to overcome difficulties they had to face, how to remain faithful in the face of persecution and scorn, his preaching on brotherly love and forgiveness of enemies. These were the Epistles.

Finally, towards 90 AD The Book of Revelation was written, the account of an extraordinary vision to comfort persecuted Christians, showing how their persecutors would be destroyed and the glory of Jesus revealed, together with the exaltation of God and adoration of the angels.

The Apostles, their Writings and their Symbols

The four apostles who wrote the gospels of the New Testament were Matthew, Mark, Luke and John. Each wanted to write the Gospel of Jesus accurately, but in his own way.

The gospels are rather like four short films which blend together and enrich each other. Jesus is always at the centre of the work, but each writer expresses his feelings and recollections in a slightly different way. This is wonderful for Christians. With four accounts seen together, we have an image of Jesus which is richer and more complete than only one record.

MATTHEW

Matthew had been a publican, that is a collector of taxes, in Capernaum. When Jesus called him, Matthew at once gave up everything to become a disciple. Matthew wrote his gospel for the Hebrews who were becoming Christians, often quoting from the Old Testament to show that Jesus was the Messiah, promised in ancient times. Matthew wrote in Arabic, but his work was translated into Greek between 70-80 AD. Traditionally, his symbol is a man, because his gospel begins the story of the coming of Jesus as a man on earth.

MARK

His full name was John Mark. Born in Jerusalem into a family from Cyprus, he spoke Greek. He was not one of the twelve disciples but perhaps knew Jesus in his youth and was a follower of Peter and St. Paul. He wrote his Gospel in Greek for pagans in Rome who

were becoming Christian. According to Biblical scholars, Mark's gospel is the oldest, completed 60-70 AD. Recently a second version was discovered, and this was older still, written little more than 20 years after the death of Christ. Mark's traditional symbol is a lion – his gospel begins with the preaching of John the Baptist in the desert where, according to ancient writers, lions roamed.

LUKE

The third apostle, Luke, was a doctor. He came from the town of Antioch in Syria, and became a Christian after being a disciple of St.Paul. He wrote his gospel in

Greek around the year 80 AD to proclaim Jesus to pagans. He wrote with care and special attention to the women who became disciples. In his gospel, the work of Jesus among the poor and the weak is recorded in particular detail. He is

also the author of the Acts of the Apostles, which tells the story of the spread of Christ's teaching and the founding of the first Christian communities. By tradition, Luke's symbol is a bull, because his gospel begins with the announcement of the angel to the priest Zechariah at the time when he was at the temple preparing for the sacrifice of animals, such as the bull.

JOHN

John was the brother of James and a friend of Peter. His gospel was written towards the end of the first century AD and in many ways is unlike the other three. He reports on episodes in the life of Jesus not recorded elsewhere and often pauses to reflect on the holiness of the Lord. The traditional symbol of John is an eagle, because, like the eagle, he was said to look upon the sun, his face shining in the reflection of Jesus.

Index